THE
HALLOWEEN
GRAB BAG

A Book of Tricks and Treats

By Ferida Wolff & Dolores Kozielski
Illustrations by David Neuhaus

HarperTrophy
A Division of HarperCollins*Publishers*

For Barrie Van Dyck with many thanks
FW

For Jennifer and Justine with love
Mom

For Sue
DN

First Harper Trophy edition

TABLE OF CONTENTS

HOW HALLOWEEN BECAME A HOLIDAY

Who doesn't love Halloween? It's the one time of the year when we dress up in costume, ask for treats, play tricks, scare and be scared. Have you ever wondered how Halloween began?

Can you find the eight Halloween objects hidden in this picture?

Answers on page 94

Halloween actually began with the Celts, an ancient people who lived more than two thousand years ago. They made their homes first in Gaul, the region we now know as France, Belgium, Western Germany, and Northern Italy. Then they migrated to England, Scotland, and Ireland.

The Celts believed everyone had a soul that lived on after death. On October 31, which was called All Hallow Even or Hallowe'en, the departed souls were supposed to come back and visit their old homes. The Druids, who were the priests and teachers of the Celts, welcomed them. But most of the Celts feared them. They disguised themselves in masks and costumes to fool the spirits and lit huge bonfires to scare them away.

Our American custom of trick or treating probably comes from Ireland. There the Celts dressed up in white robes and horsehead masks and begged for food (treats) in the name of the Druid priest Muck Olla. In exchange for the treats, the beggars offered good-luck wishes. Many years later, when Irish immigrants came to the United States, they added something new to this custom: tricks. They would soap windows, ring bells, and do other mischievous things.

Today, we celebrate Halloween by dressing up in costumes and getting and giving tricks and treats. But going out isn't the only way to have fun on Halloween. This book shows you all kinds of ways to celebrate the holiday. There are decorations to make, games to play, costumes to create, strange and wonderful recipes to try, and scary stories to tell.

Halloween comes only once a year—so let's make this the best one ever!

Watch the bat fly. Put your thumb on the edge of this book and flip the pages very quickly.

People who have triskaideka-phobia are afraid of the number 13.

CREEPY COSTUMES

What are you going to be for Halloween? How about a scary witch . . . a pirate . . . a pumpkin . . . or a dead letter? You'll find out how to be these things and many more on the next pages. See for yourself how much fun it is to make a costume that people will really notice!

Can you place each one in the right room?
Answers on page 94

MAKEUP MANIA

DON'T FORGET!

Many people have allergic reactions to makeup, so be sure to test it before you use it. At least three days before you want to wear it, rub a small amount of makeup on the inside of your wrist. Leave the makeup on for two or three hours. If it gives you a rash or starts to sting, itch, or burn, don't use it!

If you buy a Halloween makeup kit, make sure it has the FDA seal of approval. You might also try makeup that has the word "hypo-allergenic" on the label. That means the makeup is less likely to irritate your skin.

Wearing makeup can be a great part of your Halloween costume. It's amazing how much you can change your look with a few simple tricks. Here are some ideas to get you started.

With a dark-colored eyebrow pencil or powdered eye shadow, you can make:

☞ Tired eyes: Blacken the skin beneath your eyes and smudge with your fingertips.

☞ Wrinkles: Draw lines across your forehead, little lines that spread from the outer corners of your eyes, and lines from each side of your nose down to the corners of your mouth. Smudge all the lines with your fingertip.

☞ Bushy eyebrows: Brush powdered eye shadow on and above your own eyebrows.

☞ A beard and mustache: Draw many short lines on your upper lip and chin. Smudge the lines a bit with your fingers.

☞ An unshaven look: Dot the area around your mouth and chin with eyebrow pencil.

☞ Tattoos: Draw a simple figure like a snake or heart or dagger on your face, arm, or hand.

Cream eye shadow can give you a ghoulish skin color. Apply it with your fingers and smooth it all over your face.

To make blackened teeth, tear off a piece of a brown paper candy cup and press it onto the front and back of your tooth or teeth. It will stay in place, even if you talk or smile.

With hairstyling gel, you can shape your hair into spikes, antennae, grass, tops of vegetables, or slicked-back gangster hair.

Dab lipstick on your face to make spots for measles. You can also use lipstick to make war paint or a clown mouth and nose. Use blush to make rosy cheeks.

Molefoam, which you can buy in the footcare section of any drugstore, can be cut into many shapes, like moles, warts, scars, mustaches, and eyebrows. Color your shapes with powdered eyeshadow or eyebrow pencil. When the paper backing is removed, the molefoam will stick to your skin. Apply the shapes to your face and you'll fool just about everyone.

Don't forget about accessories: Fake fingernails, nail polish, glasses, wigs, hats, and ribbon all add special touches to a costume, so pile them on.

Taking it off: Most makeup comes off with cold cream or baby oil. Or follow the manufacturer's instructions for removal. Then wash your face.

In Ancient Egypt, it was the custom to draw a red circle around the mouth to keep the devil from entering the body. That may be why people started wearing lipstick.

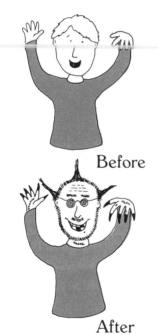

Before

After

The old saying "Blind as a bat" is untrue. Some bats can see, but most find their food by transmitting high-frequency sound waves that act like sonar to help them locate objects.

DON'T FORGET!

Be extra careful when handling needles, pins, scissors, and other sharp objects.

Make sure your costume allows you to see and breathe.

Remember to read all the instructions before beginning a project. It will be easier if you have everything on hand before you begin.

And don't be afraid to ask an adult for help if you need it!

BAT

Change into a giant bat! Flap your wings and flit through the Halloween night sky.

This is what you need:
- friend
- tape measure
- 1 yard of black felt
- chalk or pencil
- scissors
- 1 yard of black elastic, ½ inch wide
- 6 to 8 safety pins
- black ski mask
- needle and black thread
- black turtleneck or shirt and black pants or leggings
- fangs (optional)

This is what you do:
1. Spread your arms out at shoulder height. Ask your friend to measure you from wrist to wrist. Add 4 inches to that measurement.

2. Spread out the felt in a single thickness. On the long side of the material, mark off the length you just measured. Cut the felt along that mark.

3. Lie down in the middle of the piece you've just cut out, with your head extending over the edge of the fabric. Spread your arms out into a T shape. Ask your friend to mark off the places at the top edge of the fabric where your wrists and upper arms touch the felt.

4. Measure around your wrists and upper arms. Add 1 inch to each measurement. Use these lengths to cut four strips of elastic, one for each wrist and one for each upper arm.

5. Make loops of the elastic, and safety pin each loop to the top edge of the fabric at each wrist and upper-arm mark.

6. Cut the bottom of the felt in a bat-wing zigzag.

7. From the remaining felt, make two triangles for the ears, about 4 x 4 x 3 inches. Using a running stitch, sew the ears to the top of the face mask.

8. Put on your black clothes. Slip the bat wing onto your arms. Ask your friend to pin it in place at the neck and at the waist.

9. Put on the face mask. Put on the fangs, if you want to be a vampire bat.

How to make a running stitch:

Push the threaded needle through the fabric to the other side. Insert the needle back into the fabric about 1/4 inch from where you started. You've just made one stitch. Repeat this in and out pattern to make a line of stitches. Try to keep your stitches equal in length.

DEVIL

You'll set the world on fire with this Devil's costume.

This is what you need:

    10 red pipe cleaners
    rope or clothesline for the tail, cut to whatever length you wish
    red electrical tape
    scrap of red posterboard
    scissors
    36-inch tree branch, wooden dowel, or yardstick
    aluminum foil (not the heavy-duty kind)
    red turtleneck or shirt and red pants or leggings
    bobby pin
    safety pin
    black eyebrow pencil
    blush (optional)

This is what you do:

1. Make the Devil's horns first. Twist four pipe cleaners tightly together into one thick piece. Bend this piece into a crescent shape.

2. Next, make the Devil's tail. Wind electrical tape around the rope until it is entirely covered. Cut out a small triangle about 2 x 2 x 1 inches from the posterboard and tape it to the end of the tail.

3. Now make the top of the Devil's pitchfork. Twist two pipe cleaners together to make one thicker piece. Do this again two more times until you have three thick pieces. Twist the pieces together at the bottom. Curve the left and right pieces away from the one in the middle to look like a fork.

4. Tape the fork to the top of the tree branch, yardstick, or wooden dowel. Then wrap the entire pitchfork in foil. Make sure to cover the three fork pieces individually.

5. Put on your red clothes. Attach the horns to the top of your head with the bobby pin. Cover the center of the horns with your hair, so the horns look as if they are sprouting from your head. Tuck the tail into your pants or leggings and pin it in place.

6. With the eyebrow pencil, draw a thin mustache on your upper lip and a pointy beard on your chin. Draw curvy lines going upward at the outer ends of your eyebrows. If you wish, brush dark pink blush across your cheekbones, the bridge of your nose, and your forehead.

Long ago, some people thought that you could catch an evil spirit at the spot where a knot is tied.

WITCH

Feed the cat, cool down the vat, time to put on your witch's hat—you're ready for Halloween!

This is what you need:

black posterboard, about 22 x 14 inches
scissors
friend
black electrical tape
2-inch-wide black
  crepe paper streamer
tape measure
pencil
needle and black thread
glue
large rubber band
fuzzy black spiders (optional)
green cream eyeshadow
molefoam (page 11)
press-on fingernails (optional)
black turtleneck or shirt and
  black skirt or pants
cape (from vampire costume
  on page 33)

This is what you do:

1. Roll the posterboard into a cone shape to fit your head. Ask your friend to hold the cone while you tape down all the overlapping

seams with electrical tape. Cut off the extra posterboard from the bottom of the cone.

2. Measure the bottom of the cone. Cut a strip of crepe paper twice as long as the cone measurement.

3. Draw a pencil line along the length of the crepe paper, ¼ inch from the edge. Baste along the line. Gently push the crepe paper along the thread, gathering the streamer until it is the same length as the cone bottom.

4. Glue the basted edge of the crepe paper to the cone bottom. When it is dry, press the paper upward with your hands to make a brim.

5. Cut the rubber band. Poke a hole in each side of the hat. Push one end of the rubber band through each hole. Tie off each end. You may want to decorate your hat with a few fuzzy black spiders, which you can make on page 37. Stick them on with glue or tape.

How to baste:
This is just like the running stitch on page 13, except that the stitches are larger—about ½ inch long—and farther apart.

6. Rub green eyeshadow on your face and hands. Cut warts and scars from molefoam, color them with eyeshadow, and stick them on your face. You might also want to wear a set of long press-on nails.

7. Put on your black clothes and cape. Now get on your broom and go!

WIZARD

You could almost whip up this wizard's costume in the time it takes to spell A-B-R-A-C-A-D-A-B-R-A.

This is what you need:

- aluminum foil (not the heavy-duty kind)
- yarn, about 30 inches long
- posterboard, any color
- scissors
- friend
- clear plastic tape
- glue
- glitter, sequins, gold and silver markers (your choice)
- tree branch, about 24 inches long, the twistier the better
- newspaper
- fabric (an old sheet is fine) cut into a rectangle 48 x 2 inches
- silver cream eye shadow
- molefoam (page 11)
- long bathrobe

This is what you do:

1. Form a small amount of aluminum foil into a shape: a ball, crescent moon, triangle, or anything else you like. Make a small foil loop at the top of the shape. Thread the yarn through the loop and tie it around your neck. This is the wizard's amulet.

2. Make a wizard's hat, following steps 1 and 5 for the witch's hat on pages 16–17 (use clear tape rather than black). Decorate your hat by gluing on glitter or sequins instead of spiders. Or draw stars or moons on it with your markers.

3. Make a magic staff by wrapping the tree branch in foil.

4. Cover your work surface with newspaper. Spread out the fabric strip. Glue glitter or sequins, or both, onto the strip. Let dry.

5. Rub silver cream eye shadow on your face. Cut molefoam into small stars and crescent moons. Glue glitter to the material side of the foam. Remove the backing and stick the shapes to your face.

6. Put on the bathrobe, using the sequined strip as a belt. Put on the hat and amulet and carry the staff. Presto! You're a wizard!

An amulet is a charm worn around the neck to protect a person from the danger of witchcraft, the evil eye, or lightning.

DEAD LETTER

Deliver a scare—and a laugh—to your friends with this costume, straight from the Dead Letter Office.

This is what you need:
   an old, flat, twin-size white bed sheet
   friend
   pencil
   yardstick
   scissors
   newspapers
   waterproof markers
   makeup

This is what you do:

1. Fold the sheet in half, crosswise. Place it flat on the floor.

2. Lie down on the sheet as shown, with your head extending over the folded edge and one wrist extending over a side edge. Spread your arms out into a T shape.

3. Ask your friend to mark off, in pencil, the places where your

other wrist, ankles, and neck touch the sheet.

4. With your yardstick and pencil, draw lines connecting the wrist and ankle marks to form a rectangle. Then cut through both layers of the sheet along the pencil lines.

5. Cut a little scoop out of the sheet where you marked the neck. Don't make it too big! You can always enlarge it later.

6. Put several layers of newspaper between the folds of the sheet so ink won't run through to the other side. Using markers, write a scary imaginary name and address in the center of the sheet. Your address could be written in red marker with letters that look like dripping blood. Write a creepy return address in the upper left corner of the sheet. Draw a scary-looking stamp in the upper right corner.

7. Apply white cream eye shadow all over your face. Ring your eyes with gray powdered eye shadow.

8. When you greet someone, lift your arms into the T position. You're ready for the mailbox—and the dead letter office!

Q. Where did the spook buy his stamps?

JACK O'LANTERN
6 BAT WAY
COFFINVILLE

FRANK N. STEIN
13 BIG CASTLE RD.
MONSTERVILLE,
U.S.A.

A. At the ghost office.

DINNER

Dinner is served, and you are the table, the place setting, and the meal. You can make your dinner look delicious or just plain gross.

This is what you need:

clean cardboard carton (most supermarkets have a stack of empty cartons that they'll give away for free)

scissors

paper toweling

glue

transparent tape

paper plate

plastic fork, knife, and spoon

dinner-size paper napkin

paper cup

dried beans, peas, raisins, nuts, pasta, etc.

paint (optional)

This is what you do:

1. Cut a hole in the bottom of the carton large enough for your head to fit through. This is now the top of your costume. Cut a hole in each side of the carton for your arms. You may need an adult's help when you do this, since the cardboard may be thick and hard to cut. If your carton did not come with the loose flaps cut off, cut them off now.

2. Cover the outside of the carton with paper toweling and glue it down. Don't worry about covering the holes—you'll take care of that in the next step.

3. Cut away the toweling from the head and arm holes. Glue down any loose edges.

4. Choose one side of the carton to be the front. Tape the plate to the center of the box.

5. Tape the fork on the left side of the plate. Tape the knife and spoon on the right side. Tape the napkin above the plate. Tape the cup above the knife.

6. Glue dried foods to the plate. Make it colorful or make it gross. Mix up some paint and paint your food, if you wish.

A dropped fork is said to warn of a stranger's arrival. If you drop a knife, a man will visit. A spoon will bring a woman caller.

MUMMY

You and a friend could really get wrapped up making this costume! You can buy the cheesecloth from most supermarkets.

This is what you need:

pants and a long-sleeved shirt
friend
3 or 4 packages of cheesecloth (about 4 square yards per package)
7 safety pins
scissors

This is what you do:

1. Put on pants and a long-sleeved shirt.
2. Ask your friend to pin one end of the cheesecloth at your ankle, and wrap the cheesecloth upward around your entire leg. Continue wrapping the cheesecloth around your body until the cloth runs out. Pin the end in place.
3. Repeat step 2 on your other leg with another package of cheesecloth, working from your ankle to your waist.

4. Using the third package of cheesecloth, begin at the place you left off and cover your chest and one arm. Cut off any excess cloth and pin the end in place at your wrist.

5. Now wrap your other arm, beginning at the wrist. (You may need to use another package of cheesecloth to do this.) Continue upward, wrapping the cloth loosely around the neck and head. Make sure you can see and breathe. Tuck in the end.

A mummy is a dead body that had been embalmed and wrapped in linen cloth to preserve it. It was believed that anyone disturbing a mummy would be cursed.

COSTUMES FOR TWO OR MORE

These group costumes are as easy as 1-2-3! Call up your friends and make your costumes together.

PAIR OF DICE

If you and your best friend are two of a kind, you'll love wearing these outfits. Make sure your faces add up to a lucky number, and it's a sure bet you'll have a great time on Halloween.

This is what you need:

2 clean square cartons, about the same size (most supermarkets have stacks of empty cartons that they'll give away for free)

scissors

white paint

paintbrush

1 die from a pair of dice

black construction paper

wide-mouth glass

pencil

glue

white cream eye shadow

black eyebrow pencil

This is what you do:

1. Cut a hole in the bottom of one carton large enough for your head to fit through. This is now the top of your costume. Cut a hole in each side of the carton for your arms. You may need an adult's help when you do this, since the cardboard may be thick and hard to cut. If your carton did not come with the loose flaps cut off, cut them off now.

2. Paint the carton white. Let dry. Repeat these two steps for the second carton.

3. You will use the die as a model for your costume. Choose a number on the die for your face. Put the die on a table with your face number on top.

4. Count the number of dots on the four sides of the die. You will need this many circles for your costume. (You won't need to cut any circles for the top or bottom of your carton.) Using the glass, trace and cut circles from the black construction paper.

5. Glue the circles to the sides of the carton, as they appear on the die.

6. Cover your face with white cream eye shadow. With eyebrow pencil, draw on your face the number of circles you see on the top of the die. Repeat steps 3 through 6 for the second costume. Now you and your friend are ready to roll!

Evil spirits will not harm you if you stand in a circle. A circle represents the all-powerful sun, which keeps evil away.

SCHOOL OF FISH

There's nothing fishy about making this costume. It's super easy, start to finish.

This is what you need:

2 sheets of posterboard for each fish, any color

pencil

scissors

colored markers

glitter, sequins, and glue (optional)

2 yards of elastic for each fish, about ½ inch to 1 inch wide

stapler

crepe paper streamers, any color (optional)

bobby pins

cream eye shadow to match the streamers (optional)

This is what you do:

1. With the pencil, draw a large fish shape, using the entire sheet of posterboard. Cut it out.

2. Trace the fish shape onto the second posterboard sheet and cut out the second fish.

3. Place the two fish shapes mouth to mouth as if they were kissing. Now decorate your fish with marker, glitter, and sequins to make scales, stripes, dots, an eye and a mouth. Use the same design for both fish cutouts.

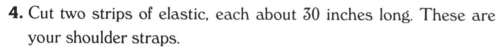

4. Cut two strips of elastic, each about 30 inches long. These are your shoulder straps.

5. Staple one shoulder strap to one of the shapes, stapling one end of the strap to the head and one end to the tail. Repeat with the second strap and the second shape.

6. Staple the fish's tail sections together. Hold the fish around your body and put your arms through the shoulder straps. Now staple the fish's nose sections together.

7. Cut four or five pieces of crepe paper to whatever length you please to make a fin for your head. You can fringe or zigzag the ends if you wish and glue on sequins and glitter for a little extra sparkle. Staple the pieces together and bobby pin it to your head, letting the end fall free. If you like, make another fin to attach to the bottom of your costume.

8. Color your face with a matching shade of cream eye shadow.

9. Repeat steps 1 through 8 for each costume. Now go out with your friends as a school of fish.

A talisman is a good-luck charm such as a scarab beetle, rabbit's foot, horseshoe, or four-leaf clover.

CHAIN GANG

Here's the perfect costume for you and the gang. The instructions below are for three friends, but link up with as many as you like—just make more chains.

This is what you need:

2 friends

plain white or gray sweatshirt and matching sweatpants

(you'll look more impressive if you all dress in one color)

2 rolls of black electrical tape

scissors

1 small piece of gray posterboard

1 box of large paper clips

brown or gray powdered eye shadow

This is what you do:

1. Tape black stripes about 4 inches apart all the way around your sweatshirt. It may be easiest for you and your friends to put on your sweats and take turns striping each other. Don't forget to stripe your arms.

2. Now stripe your pants.

3. Cut three strips about 2 x 6 inches from the posterboard. Roll the strips into cuffs and tape them closed. Ask each person to put on a cuff. Make sure each person is wearing the cuff on the same wrist.

4. Ask each person to make a bracelet chain of paper clips for the wrist, about 7 clips or more until it fits around the cuff.

5. Make a chain of 20 paper clips. Connect one end to your bracelet. Connect the other end to one of your friend's bracelets. Make another paper clip chain and connect this one to your bracelet as well. Then connect the loose end of the chain to your second friend's bracelet. If more friends want to be part of your gang, ask each one to make a cuff, bracelet, and chain, and connect the chain to the last person in line.

6. With your finger, draw a line of brown or dark gray powdered eye shadow across your forehead, down each cheek, and across your chin. Smudge the lines so they look like dirt.

7. Walk together like prisoners on a chain gang.

Q. Why couldn't the ghost ride the bus?

A. Because he didn't have exact chains.

HURRY-UP COSTUMES

Here are some super costumes you can make in a flash.

BLACK CAT

Put on a black turtleneck and pants. Make a tail by stuffing one black knee-high stocking with tissues. Pin on the tail with a safety pin. Cut out two ears from black felt and use electrical tape to attach them to a thin black headband. Draw on whiskers and a nose with black eyebrow pencil.

PUMPKIN

Put on black or orange pants and a long-sleeved shirt. Poke two holes for your legs in the bottom of a pumpkin trash bag and a hole in the each side for your arms. Put on the bag with the pumpkin face in front and stuff it with newspaper. Tie the bag loosely at your neck. Color your face with green cream eye shadow. Slick up your hair into spikes with styling gel.

VAMPIRE

Put on black pants and a turtleneck. Cut open a black drawstring trash bag from one of the string openings to the bottom of the bag. Gather the plastic toward the middle along the drawstrings. Cut along the bottom to even the cape and tie the cape around your neck. Smear white cream eye shadow over your entire face. Put on red lipstick and draw red lines dripping down from the corners of your mouth. Put on a pair of fangs and slick back your hair with styling gel.

PIRATE

Get an old pair of pants and a shirt you can cut. Cut zig-zags on the bottom edges of your pant legs, shirt, and sleeves. Put on the clothes, letting your shirt hang out of your pants. Wear a thick belt or tie a colorful scarf around your waist. Tie a bandanna on your head. Make beard marks on your face with eyebrow pencil. Smear dark blue and black cream eye shadow around one eye for a black eye. Tie a hoop earring around one ear.

If a black cat crosses in front of you, it brings bad luck. If it walks toward you, however, good luck comes with it.

CRAWLY CRAFTS

Spook your friends with a big, fuzzy spider. Light up your house with a jack-o'-lantern. Turn your room into a haunted graveyard. All the makings are here . . . to transform your house into a hair-raising holiday feast for the eyes and ears!

Help the ghost haunt the house.
Lead him through the maze to his victim.
Answer on page 94

It is believed that evil spirits can be prevented from entering your home if the key is left in the keyhole.

THE WELCOME WEB

Here's a creepy way to greet anyone who enters your house.

This is what you need:

    construction paper or posterboard
    scissors
    ruler
    fishing line or fine black thread
    transparent tape

This is what you do:

1. Cut a strip of paper or posterboard the width of your doorway and about 2 inches wide. (If you use construction paper, you will probably have to tape two or more pieces end to end.) The strip will be harder to see if it's the same color as your doorway.

2. Measure the distance between the top of your doorway and the top of your head. Then add 6 inches to that measurement.

3. Cut about 30 lines of thread at the measurement you figured out in step 2. If some of your friends are shorter than you, cut some longer threads as well. You should have enough thread lines to

put across the paper strip but not so many that they are easily seen.

4. Tape one end of each thread to the paper strip.

5. Tape the strip with the threads attached to the inside of the doorway. Anyone entering will have to pass through the line of threads. It will feel exactly like walking through a web.

SPIDERS, SPIDERS EVERYWHERE

What could be spookier than a wall full of big, hairy, black spiders? They also make great pets—and they're perfect for frightening friends.

This is what you need:

1 ball of black yarn

scissors

black pipe cleaners (you'll need 4 for each spider you make)

glue

transparent tape or thread

DON'T FORGET!

It never hurts to play it safe. Be extra careful when handling needles, pins, scissors, and other sharp objects.

Remember to read all the instructions before beginning a project. It will be easier if you have everything on hand before you begin.

And don't be afraid to ask an adult for help if you need it!

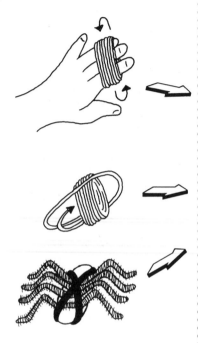

The fear of spiders is called arachnophobia. It is thought that if you kill a spider, it will bring bad luck.

This is what you do:

1. Hold two or three of your middle fingers together. (The more fingers you use, the larger your spider body will be.) Wrap the yarn 12 times loosely around your fingers.

2. Gently work the little tube of yarn off your fingers. Then wrap the yarn 12 times across the tube, forming a solid black oval. This is the spider's body.

3. Holding the pipe cleaners across the spider's body, wrap the yarn around them diagonally in two directions, forming an X. Wrap a second X on top of the first.

4. Cut the yarn. Glue the loose end onto the spider's body.

5. Spread and shape the pipe cleaners so that they look like spider legs.

6. Roll a piece of transparent tape into a loop with the sticky sides facing out. Use the loop to attach your spider to a wall. Or tie thread to your spider's body and hang it from a doorway.

7. Now that you've made one, make more! Put together an army of five or six spiders to crawl or hang anywhere you wish.

GHOSTS

You'll want to make lots of these friendly ghosts to hang around the house and keep you company on Halloween night.

This is what you need:
>1 package of white paper napkins
>1 bag of large cotton balls
>white thread
>black marker

This is what you do:

1. Unfold a napkin and lay it flat on a table.
2. Place one cotton ball in the center of the napkin and gather the napkin around it. Tie the thread around the napkin to make a neck. The wrapped cotton ball is the ghost's head.
3. Draw eyes (and a mouth, if you wish) on your ghost with the marker.
4. Make as many ghosts as you want and hang them around the house as decorations.

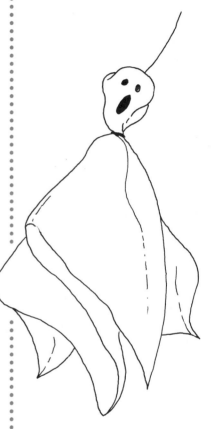

JACK-O'-LANTERN

It won't feel like Halloween without a jack-o'-lantern to light up your house. But pumpkin carving is a messy business, so put on your old clothes before you dig in.

This is what you need:

newspapers
pumpkin
marker or pen
sharp knife
spoon
votive candle
long match

DON'T FORGET!
Pumpkins are hard to cut. Make sure you get an adult to help you carve—you want to cut the pumpkin, not yourself!

This is what you do:

1. Before you carve, cover your work surface with newspapers.

2. Draw a circle around the pumpkin stem. Make it large enough for your fist to comfortably fit through the hole when it is cut. Now get an adult to help you cut out the circle. Slant the cuts inward toward the stem, so the bottom of the lid is smaller

than the top. Remove the lid from the pumpkin.

3. Reach inside the pumpkin and pull out the seeds, strings and all. When you have pulled out as many of the seeds as you can by hand, scrape out the rest with the spoon. Set the seeds aside. (We show you how to roast them on page 71.)

4. Draw a face or a Halloween design on the pumpkin. Use any shapes you want. Just remember, the smaller the shapes, the harder they are to cut out. Now get an adult to help you cut out your design.

5. Select a safe place to display your jack-o'-lantern. Make sure that it's a good distance away from anything that can catch fire. Put the votive candle inside and light the candle with the long match.

SCARECROW

Your scarecrow doesn't have to scare birds away. You can make it as scary or funny as you like. Dress it up to look like a famous person or a member of the family.

The movement of a scarecrow by the wind is supposed to frighten away birds, especially crows, from crops in the field.

This is what you need:

old plain pillowcase, any color

newspaper

scissors

yarn

markers

bowtie, funny nose glasses (optional)

glue

old shirt, pants, mittens or gloves, socks, and shoes

safety pins

leaves

This is what you do:

1. Stuff the pillowcase with newspaper. Tie it closed with yarn. Then draw a face on the pillowcase with your markers. If you want to make a funny scarecrow, tape a pair of funny nose glasses to the pillowcase.

2. Cut yarn for the hair and glue it in place.

3. Stuff the shirt, mittens, and pants with newspapers. Tuck the shirt into the pants, and tuck the mittens into the shirtsleeves. Stuff the socks and tuck them into the pant legs, then into the shoes.

4. Tuck the pillowcase into the neck of the shirt. Safety pin it in place. Tuck leaves around the neck, wrists, waist, and pant legs. Put a bowtie on your scarecrow, if you wish.

5. Prop up your scarecrow in a corner, against a doorway, on a chair, or near a window.

SPIDER MUMS

A "boo-quet" of spider mums is the perfect decoration for a Halloween table. Chrysanthemums (often called mums, for short) are plants that flower in late summer through fall. The flowers come in a great variety of colors and petals.

This is what you need:

    black or orange wide curling ribbon, or both

    scissors

    black or orange pipe cleaners, or both

    vase

    twigs, branches, dead flowers (optional)

Q. What position does a monster play on the soccer team?

A. Ghoulie.

The amethyst, a purple gemstone, was said to protect its wearer from poison, plague, toothaches, and headaches, and to ward off evil spells.

This is what you do:

1. For each flower, cut four or five strips of ribbon, each about 8 inches long.

2. Hold the ribbon strips together and wind one end of a pipe cleaner three times around the middle of the strips to make the center of the flower. The remainder of the pipe cleaner is the stem. You can change the length of the stem by winding the pipe cleaner more times around the middle.

3. Tear each end of ribbon into three or four strips toward the pipe-cleaner center. Press the torn strips downward.

4. Arrange the flowers in a vase or other container. You may want to add dead flowers and twigs or branches from shrubs to complete your arrangement.

BEANBAG BATS

What's fuzzy and black, flies, and is full of beans? These beanbag bats! You'll need to do a little sewing to make them, but they'll be in the air sooner than you think.

This is what you need:

1 sheet of loose-leaf paper or tracing paper

pencil

scissors

safety pins

1 black felt "square" (available in fabric stores)

chalk

needle

black thread

16-ounce bag of dried peas or small dried beans

bottle of whiteout or pair of small toy eyes (you can buy them
   in most art supply stores)

glue

This is what you do:

1. Trace the bat patterns on page 47 onto the paper and cut them out.

2. Pin the patterns onto the felt. With the chalk, trace around the patterns. Unpin the patterns and cut out the bat shapes.

3. Fit the bat front to the center of the bat back and sew them together using the running stitch (page 13). Keep your stitches

A gremlin is a supernatural being that is supposed to cause trouble on airplanes.

small and about ¼ inch from the edge of the material. Leave the top open to form a pocket.

4. Fill the pocket with the peas or beans. Sew the opening closed.

5. On the front of the bat, dot on two eyes with whiteout, or glue on two small toy eyes. Let the eyes dry. Make as many bats as you wish. Then toss them around to make them fly. Or make The Bell Tower (page 48) and play a bat-toss game with your friends.

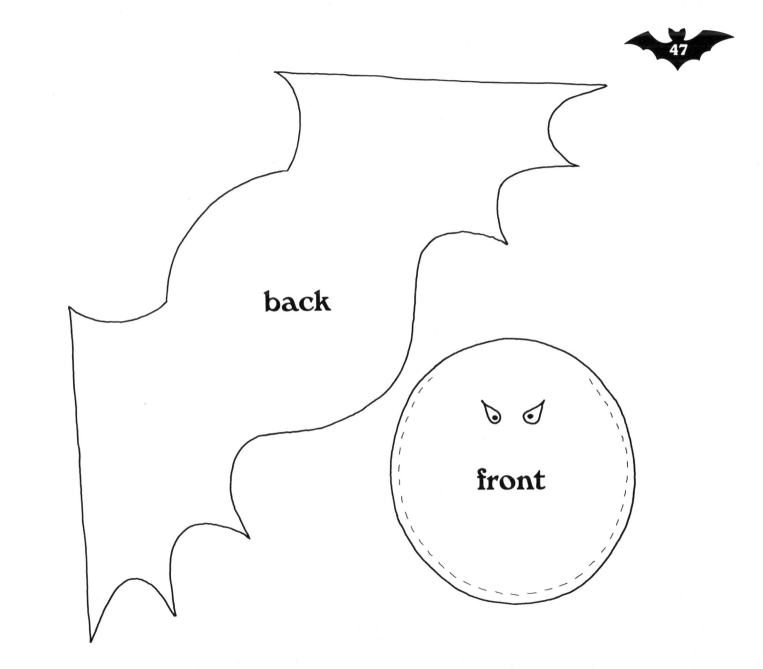

back

front

According to Sicilian folklore, bats have the face of the Devil and are thought to bring disease.

THE BELL TOWER

Here's a place for your bats to hang out.

This is what you need:

medium-sized rectangular
cardboard carton (make sure
it has all its flaps)
packing tape
5 or 6 paper clips
small bell
black and red crayons
black construction paper
scissors

This is what you do:

1. Stand the carton up on its short end.
2. Open all the flaps. Pull up the top flaps to form a triangle on top of the carton. This will be the bell-tower roof. Tape the top of the roof closed.
3. Pull the side flaps together and tape them flat to the carton.

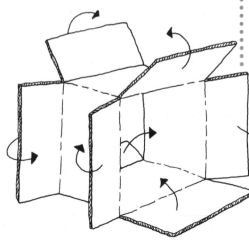

Repeat this on the other side.

4. Pull the bottom flaps straight up and tape them to the box.

5. Make a chain of 5 or 6 paper clips. Tape one end of your chain to the inside top center of the carton. Attach the bell to the last clip on the other end of the chain.

6. Color the roof with black crayon. Draw a brick pattern in red crayon all around the outside of the bell tower.

7. From the black construction paper, cut out a few bats (you may want to use the back pattern on page 47) and use them to decorate your tower. You're ready to play the Bats in the Bell Tower game on page 86.

TOMBSTONES

Transform any room into an eerie graveyard with these tombstones.

This is what you need:
>   several large sheets of gray posterboard
>   pencil

Many cultures believe certain people have "the evil eye," which can cause illness or death just by looking at you.

scissors

black marker

stencil or black stick-on alphabet letters (optional)

transparent tape

This is what you do:

1. Draw lines to divide each posterboard into six equal portions. Cut along the lines.

2. Cut tombstone shapes from the posterboard sections. (The easiest way to make them is to round off the top corners of the board with your scissors.)

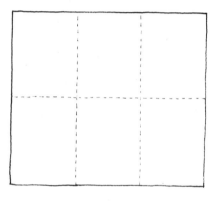

3. In the middle of each tombstone, write an epitaph, using marker, stick-on letters, or a stencil. Stick-on letters or a stencil will make your epitaphs look more formal.

4. Tape the tombstones in place on the wall.

5. To make freestanding tombstones, bend an entire sheet of gray posterboard into three equal sections. Open up the posterboard.

6. Draw a curved tombstone shape at the top of each section. Cut

around each curve, leaving the tombstones connected.

7. Write an epitaph in each tombstone section.

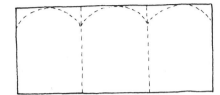

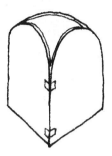

8. Bend the tombstones along the fold lines so the epitaphs face out. Tape the free sides together so that the bottom of the poster-board forms a triangle.

9. Use the tombstones to decorate your Halloween table or stand them anywhere you want to create an instant graveyard.

The ringing of bells, especially church bells, was thought to drive away evil spirits.

TORTURE TAPE

You'll be amazed at how many scary sounds you can record on your torture tape. Use your imagination, and don't be afraid to experiment—some of the best sounds come out of everyday objects.

This is what you need:

tape recorder

blank tape

props (see suggestions below)

This is what you do:

1. Put the blank tape in the tape recorder. Then tape a spooky sound, such as a slamming door, and immediately turn the recorder off. The idea is to not have any spaces between the taped sounds. Record more sounds. You may want to repeat some. You don't have to make the tape all at once. You can record the sounds over several days. Make your tape as long as you like.

2. Play the tape whenever you want to create a scary mood.

Here are some suggestions to get you started. How many other weird sounds can you come up with?

background screaming
popping of bubblewrap
close-up screaming
crumpling of newspaper
rap music without lyrics
foot stomping
banging pots and pans
scary laughter
barking or howling dog
rattling chains
ringing telephone
playing-card shuffling
static on TV or radio
large posterboard
   shaking (thunder)
thumping fist in large
   open book (heartbeat)

faraway groaning
boiling water
scraping of a metal spoon
   against a metal bowl
hammering on wood
shower running (rain)
lower keys on a piano (rumbling)
creaky door
panting
siren
loud ticking of a clock
foot shuffling
wind howling

TRICKS AND TREATS

Learn how to send messages in invisible writing. Brew up a batch of bloody, hot spiders for family and friends. Unscramble the secret answer to a Halloween riddle . . . and that's just the beginning! There are tons of tasty treats, perplexing puzzles, and brainteasing tricks on the following pages. Ready? Trick or Treat!

Eleven things are wrong with this picture.
Do you know what they are?

Answers on page 94

INVISIBLE WRITING

Here's a great way to send your friends secret messages—in ghostly invisible writing. You'll need a sheet of white paper, a white birthday candle, some food coloring, and a paintbrush. With the candle, print your secret message. To read it, brush food coloring over the paper. (Watercolor paints will also do the trick.)

DRACULA'S LIPS

Don't let their looks fool you—these ghastly lips are really delicious! This recipe makes four pairs.

A curse is a powerful wish summoning evil. If you do not believe in the magical power of the curse, however, it loses its power.

DON'T FORGET!
Be a careful cook. Always get your parents' permission and help before using the stove and oven. Handle all knives and cooking utensils with special care.

This is what you need:
   1 red apple
   knife
   ½ cup of peanut butter or marshmallow creme
   1 large marshmallow
   red food coloring

This is what you do:

1. Cut the apple into eight full-length pieces. Remove the core but leave the skin.

2. Stack two apple slices so that their core edges touch and their skin sides face you. This is one pair of lips. Make three more pairs with the rest of the slices.

3. Spread about 2 tablespoons of peanut butter or marshmallow creme between each pair of lips to hold them together.

4. Cut the marshmallow in half, and cut each half in half again. Now cut each piece in half again. You'll have eight marshmallow fangs when you're through.

5. Press two of the fangs into the peanut butter on each pair of lips. Dab a little red food coloring on the end of the fangs to make your lips look even more gruesome.

THE TOOTHPICK TRICK

When does $18 - 6 = 5$? Only on October 31! Don't try this on a test. This is strictly Halloween math.

A lad-der lean-ing against a wall forms a sacred triangle. By walking under it, you break the magic, challenging the Devil and bringing bad luck.

Take 18 toothpicks and arrange them in this pattern:

Can you remove six toothpicks so that you will have five left? Once you figure out the answer, try this trick on your friends.

Answer on page 95

HOT SPIDERS

Who would guess that you could make hot spiders out of plain old hot dogs? This easy recipe will tickle your insides.

This is what you need:

hot dogs (at least one hot dog per person)
cutting board
knife
medium-size pot or saucepan
water
long-handled fork or tongs

plate
ketchup (optional)

This is what you do:

1. Put a hot dog on the cutting board. Carefully cut each end in half almost to the middle of the hot dog. Leave about an inch in the center uncut.

2. Turn the hot dog over so that the uncut side faces up. Make a second set of cuts like the first. Cut all the way through the meat.
3. Repeat these two steps with the rest of the hot dogs.
4. Put the hot dogs into the pot. Pour in just enough cold water to cover them.
5. Put the pot on the stove and bring the water to a boil over medium-high heat. Boil the hot dogs for about 5 minutes. The cut ends will curl as they cook, giving you spiders with curled-up legs.
6. Carefully remove the spiders from the pot with a fork or tongs and serve them on a plate.
7. Want to make bloody hot spiders? Put ketchup on them before serving.

DON'T FORGET!
Get an adult to help you with the stove.

BACKWARD SPELLS

Every witch knows a few magical Halloween words. Now you can, too. These words are special because they make sense whether you spell them forward or backward. For example, snip spelled backward is pins. Here are some for you to try:

1. a) You find these on a witch's face. _ _ _ _ _
   b) A witch's broom is made of this. _ _ _ _ _
2. a) This is what Dracula turns into. _ _ _
   b) Pull this to open a can. _ _ _
3. a) He has a red tail and horns. _ _ _ _ _
   b) What zombies once did. _ _ _ _ _
4. a) A witch's cauldron is a large one of these. _ _ _
   b) The part of Frankenstein's head that's flat. _ _ _
5. a) These are sharp-toothed rodents with long tails. _ _ _ _
   b) You might find this on the end of a magic wand. _ _ _ _
6. a) Vampires do this during the day. _ _ _ _ _
   b) This is what is left after you eat oranges. _ _ _ _ _

Answers on page 95

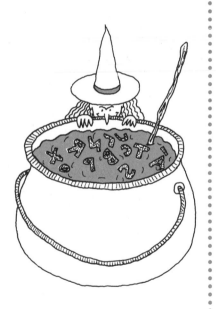

DEVIL'S BREW

Devil's Brew will surprise you and your friends. Take a sip. A second later you'll get a fizzy little "kick" on your tongue or throat. This recipe serves one.

This is what you need:

    10-ounce glass

    4 ounces of apple juice

    1 hot cinnamon ball or 8 to 10 red-hot candies

    spoon

    3 ounces of ginger ale

This is what you do:

1. Put the apple juice into the glass.

2. Add the cinnamon ball or red-hot candies to the juice and let the candy sit for 5 minutes.

3. Stir the juice to mix up the partially dissolved candy.

4. Pour in the ginger ale and mix gently.

5. Serve immediately.

Q. Why did the ghost rush home from school?

A. To watch an after-ghoul special on TV.

HALLOWEEN WORD SCRAMBLE

What did the jack-o'-lantern turn into when it fell off the porch? To find out, unscramble the Halloween words below and write them in the blank spaces. Then unscramble the letters in the circles to get the answer to the riddle.

CIWHT   _ _ _ _ ◯   IMUSQR   ◯◯_ _ _ _

LOGUH   _ _ _ ◯ _   RACES   ◯_ _ _ _

NCDAY   _ ◯ _ _ _

Unscramble the answer here: _ _ _ _ _ _ _

Answer on page 95

WITCH LIGHT

On Halloween night, a witch prepares to brew a magic potion. She gets out her book of spells and a candle to read by. She lays the logs beneath her cauldron. Then she goes to her cupboard to get matches to light the logs and the candle. But there is only one match. Which does she light first?

Answer on page 95

GHOST'S SEARCHWORD

Boo! There's a spook hiding in the letters. There's a witch on her broom. There's an owl with a hoot. They're all waiting for you to find them. There are at least 41 Halloween words in this puzzle. Look for them up and down, side to side, and corner to corner. They're tricky. Some may even be backward. Can you find them all?

```
O  K  N  O  C  K  H  O  L  B  S  B  R
T  O  L  L  P  P  C  L  D  E  V  I  L
R  O  W  I  T  C  H  I  L  L  A  P  I
N  O  O  H  O  K  A  Y  R  L  M  U  W
H  A  I  T  O  O  L  N  D  T  P  M  I
E  D  O  O  H  O  L  K  D  R  I  P  N
D  O  O  M  G  H  O  S  T  L  R  K  G
A  O  G  B  A  T  W  A  N  D  E  I  S
B  R  O  O  M  O  E  M  O  D  B  N  T
L  E  E  L  M  F  E  K  O  O  P  S  A
A  G  X  B  B  O  N  E  S  O  O  D  E
C  A  T  O  O  W  R  G  E  F  N  S  R
K  R  A  D  T  L  C  O  F  F  I  N  T
```

Answers on page 95

Answers on page 95

HINT

These are the words to look for:

BAT	IMP
BELL	KNOCK
BLACK	LOOT
BLOB	MASK
BLOOD	MOAN
BONES	MOON
BOO	NOOSE
BROOM	OWL
CANDLE	PUMPKINS
CAT	RIP
CHILL	SPOOK
COFFIN	TOMB
DARK	TOOTH
DEVIL	TREAT
DOOM	TRICK
DOOR	VAMPIRE
FOOD	WAND
GHOST	WHOO
HALLOWEEN	WINGS
HOOT	WITCH
HOWL	

If garlic is worn around the neck, it is thought to keep the soul from leaving the body and the Devil from entering.

VAMPIRE ICE CUBES

This super-easy recipe will give the shivers to your friends!

This is what you need:

2 ice cube trays (this will make about 28 cubes)
32-ounce bottle of cranberry juice cocktail

This is what you do:

1. Fill the ice cube trays with cranberry juice cocktail instead of water. Put the trays into the freezer.
2. When the cubes are frozen, use them in light-colored drinks like ginger ale or water. They will "bleed" as they melt.

BATWING CROSSWORD PUZZLE

Even though Dracula hates crosses, he couldn't escape being included in this Halloween puzzle. Four batwings are also hidden here. Can you find them?

Answers on page 95

ACROSS

3. A famous vampire.
6. Nightmare on Elm Street is a scary one.
9. Passed away.
10. A witch's poisoned present.
11. A frightening line on Frankenstein's face.
12. Poisonous snakes.
13. A synonym for yell.
14. Fishnet is made of this.
15. ___man (a word game).
18. Halloween month.

DOWN

1. A vampire's flying form.
2. This could hold a poisoned drink.
4. Another word for hags.
5. _____ Lizards! (an exclamation).
7. A swampy place.
8. A ghost is also this.
9. The opposite of life.
16. The abbreviation for streets.
17. The alphabet begins with these letters.

WHOLE-WHEAT WITCH

This isn't just a sandwich—it's a sand-witch! And it's just the thing to have when the Halloween hungries get you. Save any leftover bread scraps to feed the birds.

This is what you need:

> 3 slices of whole-wheat bread
> plate
> wide-mouthed glass
> peanut butter
> knife
> jelly
> raisins
> pretzel sticks

This is what you do:

1. Put a slice of the bread on the plate. With the glass, cut a circle from the middle of the bread. Repeat with the second slice.
2. Spread peanut butter on one of the circles.
3. Cut a long triangle from the third piece of bread. Place the bot-

tom edge of the triangle on top of the circle as a hat. Spread jelly on the second bread circle and put it on top of the first bread circle and the hat bottom.

4. Put a face on your witch. Dab two spots of peanut butter where the eyes should be, and stick raisins on each dab. Spread a little peanut butter into a mouth shape and cover with raisins. Press a whole pretzel stick in the center of the witch's face for the nose.

5. Spread the hat with peanut butter. Place several whole pretzel sticks on the edge of the hat to make a brim. Fill in the rest of the hat with pretzel pieces. Hungry? Then cast a spell on the witch and make her disappear!

Q. Why did the witch hold her nose?

KNOCK, KNOCK, WHO'S THERE?

Nine spooks knocked at the door of the haunted house, but one got scared when the door opened and hid in the bush. Two goblins knocked and went in. Five ghosts knocked, but three flew away before anyone answered. How many knocked at the door in all?

Answer on page 96

A. Because she smelled a terrible ogre.

The famous magician Harry Houdini died on Halloween 1926. He claimed that after his death he would send a message to his wife through a secret code.

CRYPTO-WORDS

There's a secret message hidden in the answers to these questions. To figure out what it is, read each sentence and guess the word it's describing. The blank spaces show you how many letters are in each word. Write the words in order and run them together. Then separate them into new words.

1. You use this to fill up tires. _ _ _ _
2. Another word for relative. _ _ _
3. Delicious Halloween desserts. _ _ _ _
4. The sense belonging to your mouth. _ _ _ _ _
5. Opposite of bad. _ _ _ _
6. One position for a light switch. _ _
7. Another word for corridor. _ _ _ _
8. To be in debt. _ _ _
9. Not the beginning. _ _ _
10. The Star-Spangled Banner begins with this. _ _
11. Abbreviation of avenue. _ _ _
12. Not all. _ _ _ _

Answers on page 96

WIGGLY BATS

These yummy bats can't fly, but they'll wiggle and squiggle plenty before you pop them in your mouth.

This is what you need:

 2   3-ounce packages of orange gelatin
 2 packets of unflavored gelatin
 2 large bowls
 2 ½ cups of orange juice
 medium-size pot
 spoon
 12-ounce bag of semi-sweet chocolate morsels
 measuring cup
 ladle
 glass pan, approximately 13 x 9 inches
 bat or star cookie cutter
 knife and spatula

This is what you do:

1. Put the orange gelatin and unflavored gelatin into one of the

Q. Why does Dracula like to play on the all-vampire baseball team?

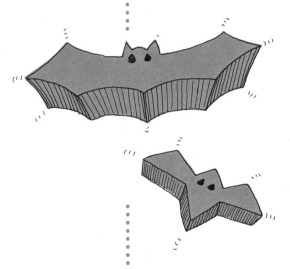

A. Because he's always next to bat.

DON'T FORGET!
Get an adult to help you with the stove.

bowls and set aside.

2. Pour the orange juice into the pot and heat it until it boils. Then pour the hot juice into the bowl of gelatin. Stir until the gelatin is dissolved.

3. Put 1 ½ cups of the morsels into the pot. Melt the chocolate on low heat, stirring constantly. (Chocolate burns easily, so keep the heat low.) When all the chocolate has melted, pour it into the gelatin mixture and stir until the mixture turns a solid brown color.

4. Ladle the mixture into the glass pan and cool in the refrigerator for at least three hours, until it is completely set.

5. Cut bat shapes out of the gelatin with your cookie cutter. Remove the bats with the spatula. A bat cookie cutter will make one dozen wiggly bats. If you are using the star cookie cutter, cut star shapes in the gelatin. Then use the knife to cut an "M" from edge to edge in the middle of each star. The portion with three points is your wiggly bat. A star cookie cutter makes 15 wiggly bats. You may want to press two chocolate morsels into each wiggly bat for eyes.

6. Save the leftover gelatin for a treat on another day. You can also use some for a Haunted House Welcome (page 82).

PUMPKIN SEEDS

What do you do with the seeds left over from pumpkin carving? Eat them, of course!

This is what you need:

pumpkin seeds   paper towels   salt and spices (optional)
colander   baking sheet

This is what you do:

1. Preheat the oven to 350 degrees.

2. Separate the seeds from the strings. Put the seeds in the colander and rinse them well.

3. Lay out paper towels and spread the seeds on them to dry.

4. Arrange the dried seeds on the baking sheet in a single layer. Leave them plain or sprinkle them with salt, onion, garlic, or chili powder. Bake the seeds for about 30 minutes or until they turn golden brown. Baking time will vary depending on the number of seeds and their dryness.

DON'T FORGET!
Get an adult to help you with the baking.

Some people believe that a mirror reflects a person's soul. That is why they think breaking a mirror will bring bad luck.

THE WITCH'S SHOPPING LIST

Oops! The witch has run out of ingredients for her special Halloween potion—and because she has a bad memory, it's up to you to help her. Take a look at the ingredients she needs. You have only one minute. Now turn to page 74 and make up her shopping list. How many ingredients do you remember?

HALLOWEEN NOUNSENSE

Get together with a friend to create your own wacky version of the Frankenstein story. Without reading the story to your friend, ask for nouns, verbs, and adjectives to fill in all the blanks. Write the words your friend tells you and then read the story out loud. How funny can you get?

Frankenstein's monster was the creation of Dr. Frankenstein, a character in a book written by Mary Shelley in 1816.

One day Dr. Frankenstein made a _____ (NOUN). It was the most _____ (ADJECTIVE) thing he had ever seen. It had _____ (ADJECTIVE) legs, fourteen _____ (PLURAL NOUN) and three _____ (PLURAL NOUN). "What have I done?" said the doctor. "I've created a _____ (NOUN)!" He took it to the laboratory. It started to _____ (VERB). "Wow!" said the doctor. "I guess I'll have to _____ (VERB)." He took a scalpel and cut it from its _____ (NOUN) to its _____ (NOUN). "Stop!" it cried. "That will make me _____ (VERB)." "_____ (EXCLAMATION)!" shouted Dr. Frankenstein. "It wasn't that bad, was it?" The _____ (ADJECTIVE) thing rolled back its _____ (PLURAL NOUN). "Be careful not to _____ (VERB) for at least two _____ (PLURAL NOUN)," said Dr. Frankenstein. So the creature rested. Soon it felt like a new _____ (NOUN).

WITCH'S LIST

1
2
3
4
5
6
7
8
9
10
11
12

HALLOWEEN MAZE

Uh-oh. It's time to go. Can you get him home safely?

Answer on page 96

WHO IS DRACULA?

Dracula doesn't want anyone to know who he really is, so he's hiding his identity in this puzzle. But you can discover his secret by coloring in each box that contains one of the letters of his name.

Bram Stoker, an English author, published *Dracula* in 1897. He based his story on Hungarian beliefs about vampires.

M	R	U	A	P	Q	S	B	I	V	N	J	X
F	C	E	R	I	U	D	R	P	S	Z	Y	E
S	A	U	D	B	D	V	A	M	C	A	D	J
O	D	B	C	Z	L	U	C	W	X	L	E	N
G	A	L	A	O	C	W	L	S	H	C	G	I
H	O	T	E	G	A	O	D	Q	V	U	O	P
M	Q	I	K	O	S	X	N	F	I	R	M	G

Answer on page 96

THE BEST HALLOWEEN PARTY EVER

Want to know how to throw a great Halloween party? Here's how to do it from start to finish. With some planning and a little help from your friends and family, you'll end up having a terrific time—and a party you'll all remember long past Halloween.

Which of these witches are twins?

Answer on page 96

WANDA   WALLIS

WINNIE   WENDY   WILLA   WILMA

THE PARTY PLANNER

Let's get started! Get out your calendar—the first thing you should do is set a date for your party. Pick a day when most people can come. Then make up a guest list with the names and addresses of the people you want to invite.

TWO WEEKS BEFORE!

Kick off your party plans with ghostly "invisible" invitations. You'll need a pack of white paper, a pair of scissors, a pencil, and a white birthday candle to make them. Cut the paper into ghost shapes. Then, using the Invisible Writing method on page 56, write out your invitations. Make sure to include the date and time you'll be having the party, as well as your address and telephone number on each card. And remind your guests to dress up in costume—it wouldn't be a Halloween party otherwise! At the bottom of each card, write these directions in pencil: **To see the secret message, brush food coloring over this card.** Put your ghosts into envelopes and mail them out.

DON'T FORGET!
Always get permission from your parents before you throw a party.

You're invited to a Party!
Where: _____
When: _____
Time: _____
Phone: _____
Don't forget to wear a costume!
To see the secret message, brush food coloring over this card.

Next, start making party decorations. Check out the crafts section of this book (pages 36–53) for ideas to get you started. Don't miss the Welcome Web (page 36) or the Torture Tape (page 52). Get some friends to lend a hand making things—it's more fun that way.

THE WEEK BEFORE!

A great party calls for great food. Think about what you and your guests would like to eat. Here are some ideas:

Dracula's Lips (page 56)   Pumpkin Seeds (page 71)
Hot Spiders (page 58)   Devil's Brew (page 61)
Wiggly Bats (page 69)   Ginger Ale with Vampire Ice
Whole-Wheat Witch (page 66)   Cubes (page 64)

Mom or Dad will probably have some good suggestions, too, so get their opinion as well. After you decide on the menu, make a list of all the ingredients you'll need to buy. Flip through the rest of this section and write down all the supplies you'll need for the games and activities. Then go shopping!

At one time, children were taken outdoors and told to look at the moon to cure a cough.

If you spill salt, you will have bad luck, unless you toss more salt over your left shoulder, where the Devil lurks, as a bribe for him to leave you alone.

Now let's think about costumes. Have you made one yet? Check out the costume section of this book (pages 10–33) for ideas.

If you plan to play the Bats in the Bell Tower game at your party (page 86), now's the time to make the Beanbag Bats (page 44) and The Bell Tower (page 48).

TWO DAYS BEFORE!

Transform your ordinary house into a haunted house. Decorate the walls and windows with all the great things you've made.

Fix some food ahead of time. If you're planning to serve Vampire Ice Cubes or Wiggly Bats, you'll need to make them today.

THE DAY BEFORE!

Put together your Candy Corn Guess door prize (page 84) and find a good place for it where everyone can see it.

Get everything ready for the Haunted House Welcome (page 82).

Put together your Ghost Burster (page 87) and hang it up in

your party room. Set up the Bats in the Bell Tower game in another corner of the room.

Make some ghost place cards for your Halloween table. Make one ghost (page 39) for each guest. Drape each ghost over a small paper cup and write your guest's name at the bottom of the napkin. Put a few small candies underneath each cup.

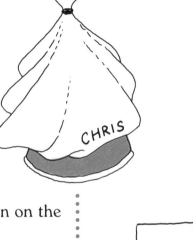

PARTY DAY!

It's here—the day you've been waiting for!

Make sure all the ingredients for the food are ready.

Put on your costume. When guests begin arriving, turn on the Torture Tape.

First, put a good scare into everyone with the Haunted House Welcome (page 82). Whatever you want to do next—eat, play games, tell stories—is up to you. At the end of the party, announce the winner of the Candy Corn Guess. And make sure each person leaves with a little bag full of treats. Had fun? Why not do it all again next year!

England, Scotland, and Wales are countries with a large number of reported house hauntings.

HAUNTED HOUSE WELCOME

Every good Halloween party has a few tricks. You'll fool everyone with this gross and gory collection. It's a great way to get your party going.

This is what you need:

10 to 12 grapes
2 plastic bags
½ box of thick spaghetti
pot filled with water
colander
1 or 2 tablespoons cooking oil
rubber glove
Welcome Web (page 36)
3 bowls
gelatin or leftover Wiggly Bat gelatin (page 69)
dish towel
Torture Tape (page 52) or scary music
blindfolds

hairy spider (page 37)
moist towels for cleanup

This is what you do:

1. Peel the grapes and put them in a plastic bag in the refrigerator.

2. Break the spaghetti in half and boil it until it's completely cooked. Drain the spaghetti in the colander and rinse it under cold running water. When it's cool, mix in one or two table-spoons of cooking oil, until the spaghetti is good and slimy. Store your spaghetti in a plastic bag in the refrigerator.

3. Fill the rubber glove with water. Tie it closed and freeze it overnight.

4. Hang the Welcome Web over the entrance to your party room.

5. On the day of your party, before your guests arrive, set out a bowl filled with the grapes, another bowl filled with spaghetti, and another bowl filled with gelatin. Put out the frozen glove and cover it with a towel.

6. Turn on some scary music or play your Torture Tape. Blindfold your guests as they arrive. Using your spookiest voice, tell them you want to share your special, secret collection with them. Then walk each person through the Welcome Web.

7. Have each person feel the grapes. Say, "These are my eyeballs."

Blue is the color most hated by witches, because it reminds them of the color of heaven.

Then have each person feel the spaghetti. Ask, "Do you like my worms?" Then have each person feel the gelatin. Say, "This is my bowl full of slug slime." Finally, tell them to shake hands with the dead hand (the rubber glove). Dangle a hairy spider across their faces. If they scream, scream with them!

CANDY CORN GUESS

Every party needs a door prize. Here is a sweet one. Make sure all of your guests take a chance.

This is what you need:
  1 glass jar, washed and dried
  1 bag of candy corn (you can also mix in gumballs and other
    small candies if you like)
  slips of paper and pencils
  1 envelope
  shoe box
  table

This is what you do:

1. Fill the jar with as much candy as you wish, counting out the candy corn as you put it in. It's easiest to do this in groups of ten. Of course, your last group probably won't be a full ten.

2. Write the number of candy corns you counted on a slip of paper and put it in the envelope.

3. Place the jar on a table next to the shoe box, slips of paper, and pencils.

4. Ask your guests to guess how many candy corns are in the jar, and to write down their guesses and their names on the slips of paper. Put their guesses in the box.

5. At the end of the party, open the envelope and the shoe box. The person who came closest to guessing the number of candy corns wins the jar of candy. If there's a tie, the winners share the candy.

In ancient times, people counted up to 12, using their 10 fingers and 2 hands. Anything over that was thought to be unlucky.

BATS IN THE BELL TOWER

Take cover—the bats are coming in for a landing! And they're aimed straight at the bell in the tower. See whose bats can wing their way to the prize!

This is what you need:

The Bell Tower (page 48)
3 Beanbag Bats (page 44)
table
prize (funny glasses, a mask, or anything
    else you can think of)

This is what you do:

1. Place The Bell Tower on a table in an area where it will be safe to toss the Beanbag Bats.
2. Stand in front of The Bell Tower. Now take four giant steps backward. This is your throw line. Take turns tossing the bats at The Bell Tower. If a bat hits the bell, you score 2 points. If a bat lands inside the tower, you score 1 point. Each person gets three tosses per turn.

3. The first person to score 15 points wins the game and gets the prize.

GHOST BURSTERS

Here's a Halloween version of a piñata that's loads of fun. You may not have enough air to blow up all the balloons yourself, so get some help. Happy ghost bursting!

This is what you need:
> white balloons (at least one per player, plus one extra for the
> ghost's head)
> small wrapped candies, dimes, and sticks of gum
> thin string and thick string
> white sheet
> black marker
> broom handle or other stick

This is what you do:
1. Blow up one balloon, knot it, and set it aside for the ghost's head.
2. Next, prepare the treats. Blow up the rest of the balloons in order

Q. What is a ghost's favorite party game?

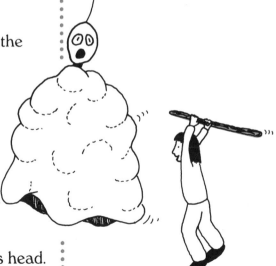

A. Hide-and-go-shriek.

to stretch them. Then release the air. Push little treats such as dimes, taffies, sourballs, or small sticks of gum through the neck of each balloon. Three or four pieces are about all that will fit without tearing a hole in the balloon.

3. Blow up the balloons again and knot the openings. Tie a different length of thin string to each balloon.

4. Tie these balloons to the head balloon. Drape the sheet over the head balloon.

5. Tie some of the thick string around the bottom of the sheet-covered head balloon to make a neck for your ghost. Leave enough string to hang it up with. Draw a face on the ghost with marker.

6. Hang the ghost from a tree in your backyard or anywhere there's enough room to safely swing the broomstick. Make sure everyone takes a turn hitting the ghost with the stick. When you pop a balloon, your turn is over. You get to keep the treats that fall to the ground! Continue playing until all the balloons are broken.

WHISPER THROUGH THE GRAVEYARD

Ask your guests to sit in a row. You will be the first person in the line, the "ghostmaster," and everyone else in line will be a ghost in the graveyard. Give everyone a pad of paper and a pencil. Write a message on your pad. Circle one word in your message—that's your secret word. Fold the paper so no one can see it. Now whisper your message to the next ghost in line. That ghost must guess your secret word and write it down before whispering the message to the next ghost. Each ghost in turn takes a guess at the secret word, writes it down, then passes on the message through the graveyard. When the last ghost has made his guess, the ghostmaster reveals the secret word. The ghost sitting closest to the ghostmaster with the correct answer becomes the new ghostmaster, and the old ghostmaster goes to the end of the line. If no one guesses the secret word, the ghostmaster continues to play until there is a new ghostmaster.

In folklore, the bogeyman was a fearsome man or spirit who used to frighten children into being good.

SCARY STORIES

Your party won't be over until you tell a good scary story—or two or three! We can get you started . . . the rest is up to you.

You'll need a tape recorder, blank tape, and a flashlight. Get the tape recorder all set to record. Turn on your flashlight, then shut off the room lights. Gather everyone around in a circle. Turn on the tape recorder. You'll start. Hold the flashlight under your chin with the light shining upward and begin telling a scary story. When you get to an exciting moment, flash off the light and pass it to the next person. The next person turns on the light and continues the story. The story ends when everyone has had a turn. If you need help getting started, try reading one of the stories below or use a story from our recommended readings list on page 93.

When your story is finished, play back the tape for everyone to hear.

THE CREAKING DOORS

Mark and Joan were on their way home from a Halloween party when the clouds that had been gathering all night burst open and dumped buckets of rain straight down on their heads. They ran to the nearest house, only to discover that it was the house everyone in the neighborhood said was haunted.

"We can't go in there," Mark whispered.

"But we can't stay out here," Joan said. She knocked on the door. No one answered. Suddenly there was a crack of thunder that made them cover their ears. Joan knocked harder. When no one came, she tried the door. Slowly, it opened. Another explosion of thunder sent them scurrying inside the house. Then, without warning, the door slammed shut.

Mark's face turned pale. "I don't care if it is raining," he cried. "I'm getting out of here!" He yanked at the doorknob, but the door didn't budge. It was locked! Just then a blinding flash lit up the room, revealing five closed doors on the opposite wall. All of the doors creaked open. Joan and Mark peeked into one of the doors and gasped. They saw . . .

People used to believe that covering their mouths when they yawned prevented the Devil from entering.

TERROR IN THE GRAVEYARD

It was mischief night, and Millie and Jason were taking their dog, Squash, out for a walk. One more block and they would be past the graveyard. Millie shivered. She had heard strange stories about the graveyard, how old man Jack, the caretaker, had seen something rise from the mist. It was last year, on this very night, that his hair had suddenly turned pure white.

"Maybe this isn't a good night to walk this way," Millie said. But Squash tugged on his leash, dragging her closer and closer toward the high iron fence. The spikes at the top of the fence jabbed at the black-purple sky. Beyond the fence, hundreds of white marble stones stuck up from the ground like crooked teeth. Before Millie knew it, the big stone angel on top of the gate was looming over them.

"Look, there's old man Jack," Jason said. Just then, an eerie green mist rose up from the ground and shrouded them all.

"I don't like this, Jason," Millie said nervously. Squash bared his teeth and growled. Suddenly, he leaped at the mist, breaking his leash, and disappeared into the creeping fog.

"Squash, come back!" Jason and Millie screamed, and ran after him. . . .

RECOMMENDED READINGS

Calhoun, Mary. *The Goblin Under the Stairs*. New York: William Morrow and Company, 1967.

Cecil, Laura. *Boo! Stories to Make you Jump*. New York: Greenwillow Books, 1990.

Gorog, Judith. *In a Messy, Messy Room*. New York: Philomel Books, 1990.

Leach, Maria. *Whistle in the Graveyard*. New York: The Viking Press, 1974.

Prelutsky, Jack. *The Headless Horseman Rides Tonight: More Poems to Trouble Your Sleep*. New York: Greenwillow Books, 1967.

Prelutsky, Jack. *Nightmares: Poems to Trouble Your Sleep*. New York: Greenwillow Books, 1967.

Sanders, Ruth Manning. *A Book of Monsters*. New York: E. P. Dutton, 1975.

These books are especially scary:

Schwartz, Alvin. *Scary Stories to Tell in the Dark*. New York: J. B. Lippincott, 1981.

Schwartz, Alvin. *Scary Stories 3: More Tales to Chill Your Bones*. New York: Harper-Collins Publishers, 1991.

According to folklore, if you find a goblin hiding in your house, you can make it do the household chores. But beware—after it has finished, it will probably create mischief.

ANSWERS TO THE TRICKS

How Halloween Became a Holiday (pages 4–5)

Creepy Costumes (pages 8–9)

The mummy is in room A; the vampire is in room B; the witch is in room C; Frankenstein is in room D; and the devil is in room E.

Crawly Crafts (pages 34–35)

Tricks and Treats (pages 54–55)

The tree has a ladder instead of a trunk; a trash can is on the roof of the house; there is a lightbulb in the candle; the center window of the house is upside down; there is a towel rack on the door; the address on the house is upside down and backward; a penguin is standing on the front step; flames are coming from the chimney; there is a backward speed-limit sign on the lawn; pumpkins are growing in the tree; the moon is facing down.

Toothpick Trick (page 58)

Remove the toothpicks marked with an X.

This is what remains.

Backward Spells (page 60)

1. a) warts b) straw; 2. a) bat b) tab; 3. a) devil
b) lived; 4. a) pot b) top; 5. a) rats b) star;
6. a) sleep b) peels.

Word Scramble (page 62)

WITCH SQUIRM GHOUL SCARE CANDY

Answer to riddle: SQUASH

Witch Light (page 62)

The match

Ghost's Searchword (page 63)

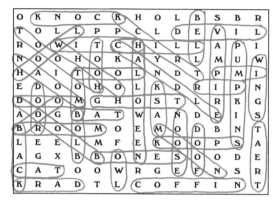

Batwing Crossword Puzzle (page 65)

The batwings are in the four corners of the puzzle.

Knock, Knock, Who's There? (page 67)

16 (they all knocked).

Crypto-Words (page 68)

1. pump, 2. kin, 3. pies, 4. taste, 5. good, 6. on, 7. hall, 8. owe, 9. end, 10. oh, 11. ave, 12. some.

Message:

Pumpkin pies taste good on Halloween. Do have some.

Halloween Maze (page 74)

Who Is Dracula? (page 75)

BAT

The Best Halloween Party Ever (pages 76–77)

WINNIE and WILMA are twins.

WALLIS is wearing glasses.

WILLA is wearing shoes with rounded toes, and she has no tooth.

WENDY does not have a wart on her nose, and her stockings are not striped.

WANDA is wearing a hat with a floppy point, and her dress has an extra button.